Author: Jed Dolton
Publisher: Daoudi Publishing
ISBN: 978-1960809056

TABLE OF CONTENT

INTRODUCTION

This book is a valuable tool for young readers, specifically designed for first-grade students who are learning to read. It focuses on the important skill of decoding words and aims to help struggling readers improve their reading abilities at the word level. The book consists of 30 reading passages, each with comprehension questions to ensure that students understand what they have read.

The passages in the book use only decodable words, which means that they are made up of letters and letter combinations that students have already learned. This approach enables children to read independently and helps them gain confidence in their reading abilities.

The book follows a structured approach, teaching children the sounds that letters make (phonemes) in a specific order. It starts with the most commonly used phonemes and progresses to more complex ones. The activities included in each passage are designed to reinforce phonemic awareness and promote skill development, such as identifying sounds, tracing letters, filling in missing letters, and more.

Whether your child is a reluctant reader or struggling with reading, this book is a valuable resource for parents and teachers. It is convenient, easy to use, and provides an effective way to help young readers build a solid foundation in reading. With the help of this book, your child will be on their way to becoming a confident and proficient reader in no time.

THIS BOOK BELONG TO

_____

I CAN READ

Read the story, and identify and underline all the - air- words.

Chair Repair

There was a little girl named Claire. She had long golden hair that shone like the sun. One day, while walking through the forest, Claire stumbled upon an old broken chair. It was in bad shape and needed some repair. With a pair of tools, she repaired the chair until it looked as good as new. Claire's friends were amazed by her talent and praised her for her repair skills. They sat down on the stairs to admire the chair and enjoyed the cool breeze in the air. They sipped tea and nibbled on cakes, feeling happy and content. Claire felt proud of herself for fixing the chair and for making her friends happy.

Answer Each Question.

Write all the "air" words you can see in the story			

THIS BOOK BELONG TO

_____

Read the story, and identify and underline all the - air- words.

Chair Repair

There was a little girl named Claire. She had long golden hair that shone like the sun. One day, while walking through the forest, Claire stumbled upon an old broken chair. It was in bad shape and needed some repair. With a pair of tools, she repaired the chair until it looked as good as new. Claire's friends were amazed by her talent and praised her for her repair skills. They sat down on the stairs to admire the chair and enjoyed the cool breeze in the air. They sipped tea and nibbled on cakes, feeling happy and content. Claire felt proud of herself for fixing the chair and for making her friends happy.

Answer Each Question.

Write all the "air" words you can see in the story			

air

I CAN READ

Read the sentences and answers the questions: Put a check mark

The car had an air bag

Jack can fix the stair

Bill will sit in a chair in the garden

Questions

What was the car equipped with?   air bag ☐   wheel ☐

What will bill sit on?   soil ☐   chair ☐

Write the correct word beside each scrambled word.

ari _____   flari _____   pari _____

chari _____   hari _____   stari _____

fria _____   lari _____   blari _____

Make sentences

Hair _____

_____

Stair _____

_____

Rules
TRACE AND COLOR

Trace it:

A A A A A A A A A A A A

a a a a a a

air air air air

Colour it:

Rules
TRACE AND COLOR

Color Me!

stair

Circle the - air - words

day	pair	mom
lair	dog	fair
stair	air	joan

Trace the words

hair   hair
pair   pair
lair   lair

Fill in the missing letters

mai _____   hai _____

wai _____   lai _____

pai _____   fai _____

Read and Trace the sentence.

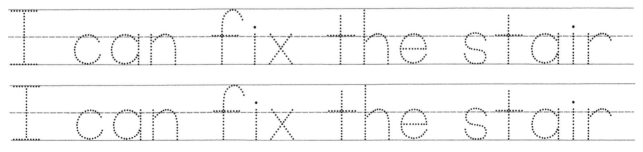

I can fix the stair
I can fix the stair

4

air

READ AGAIN

Read the story, and answer each question. highlight the answers in the story.

Chair Repair

There was a little girl named Claire. She had long golden hair that shone like the sun. One day, while walking through the forest, Claire stumbled upon an old broken chair. It was in bad shape and needed some repair. With a pair of tools, she repaired the chair until it looked as good as new. Claire's friends were amazed by her talent and praised her for her repair skills. They sat down on the stairs to admire the chair and enjoyed the cool breeze in the air. They sipped tea and nibbled on cakes, feeling happy and content. Claire felt proud of herself for fixing the chair and for making her friends happy.

Answer Each Question.

1 - What did Claire find in the forest?

_____

2 - What was wrong with the chair?

_____

3 - How did Claire repair the chair?

_____

air

COLOR ME

Read and color the Letter

Read the story, and identify and underline all the - ai- words.

Kai's Rainy Adventure

Kai once traveled by train to see his cousin. He heard the raindrops pounding against the glass and saw it raining outside the window. That day he had mailed a letter to his cousin, and he was eager for her to read it. He noticed a sailboat with a snail crawling over the deck while he was on the train. The train eventually arrived, and he met up with his cousin. They had fun while pretending to sail a boat in the rain and encountered a helpful snail in the yard. For the two cousins, it was a day full of fun and exploration.

Answer Each Question.

Write all the "ai" words you can see in the story			

ai

I CAN READ

Read the sentences and answers the questions: Put a check mark

My hair is wet

The rain made puddles

Luna paid her bill at the shop

SHOP

Questions

What did the rain make?   puddles ☐   fatigue ☐

What did luna doing?   paid the bill ☐   play ☐

Write the correct word beside each scrambled word.

fali	————	nali	————	padi
hali		jali		stari
gani		adi		pari

Make sentences

Paid

Rain

Trace it:

AI AI AI AI AI

ai ai ai ai ai ai

paid paid paid

Colour it:

ai

I CAN WRITE

Color Me!

Circle the – ai – words

ail	say	eat
cat	nail	fair
joan	far	pay

Trace the words

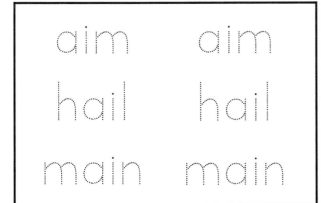

aim   aim

hail   hail

main   main

Fill in the missing letters

fali _____   padi _____

adi _____   trani _____

ladi _____   rani _____

Read and Trace the sentence.

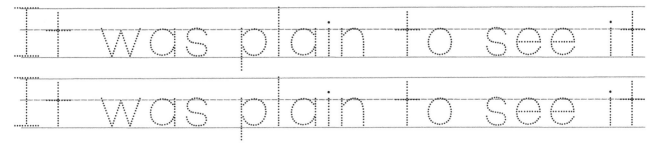

It was plain to see it

It was plain to see it

ai

READ AGAIN

Read the story, and answer each question. highlight the answers in the story.

Kai's Rainy Adventure

Kai once traveled by train to see his cousin. He heard the raindrops pounding against the glass and saw it raining outside the window. That day he had mailed a letter to his cousin, and he was eager for her to read it. He noticed a sailboat with a snail crawling over the deck while he was on the train. The train eventually arrived, and he met up with his cousin. They had fun while pretending to sail a boat in the rain and encountered a helpful snail in the yard. For the two cousins, it was a day full of fun and exploration.

Answer Each Question.

1 - Who did Kai travel to see by train

_____

2 - What did Kai hear and see outside the train window?

_____

3 - What did Kai mail to his cousin that day?

_____

ai

COLOR ME

Read and color the Letter

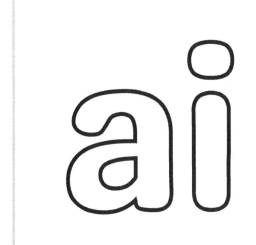

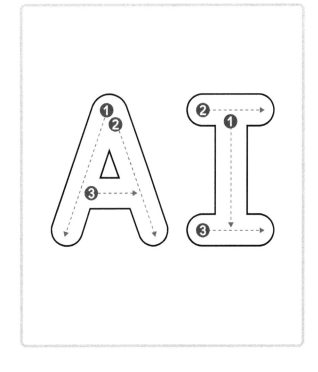

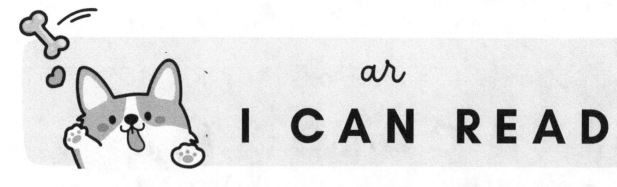

ar

I CAN READ

Read the story, and identify and underline all the - ar- words.

Lost Car

Carly and her family went to the park. Carly saw a big, green jar filled with candy. She wanted to try it, but her mom said it was too far away. Carly didn't want to get in the car to go to the jar, so she ran instead. Her dad followed, and they raced to the jar. They arrived out of breath, but happy. Carly's dad used a long bar to reach the jar and took out a piece of candy. They all shared the candy, and it tasted like heaven. Carly felt like a star because she had run so fast to get the candy.

Answer Each Question.

Write all the "ar" words you can see in the story			

ar

I CAN READ

Read the sentences and answers the questions: Put a check mark

Jon plays in the public park

He is studying hard

Our farm has a barn

Questions

Where is Jon playing?	public park ☐	stadium ☐
What's on the farm?	animals ☐	barn ☐

Write the correct word beside each scrambled word.

banr _____	atr _____	fra _____
cadr _____	cra _____	patr _____
patr _____	jra _____	yadr _____

Make sentences

Yard _____

_____

Part _____

_____

Trace it:

AR AR AR AR

ar ar ar ar

car car car car

Colour it:

I CAN WRITE

Color Me!

far

Circle the - ar - words

ail	say	jar
art	nail	cart
joan	far	pay

Trace the words

far   far
part   part
park   park

Fill in the missing letters

ta ____   car ____

ja ____   par ____

fa ____   mar ____

Read and Trace the sentence.

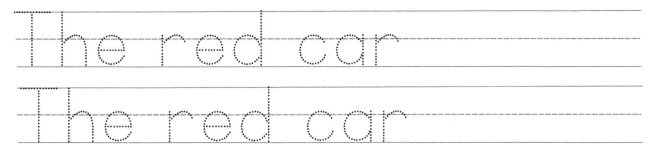

The red car

The red car

READ AGAIN

Read the story, and answer each question. highlight the answers in the story.

Lost Car

Carly and her family went to the park. Carly saw a big, green jar filled with candy. She wanted to try it, but her mom said it was too far away. Carly didn't want to get in the car to go to the jar, so she ran instead. Her dad followed, and they raced to the jar. They arrived out of breath, but happy. Carly's dad used a long bar to reach the jar and took out a piece of candy. They all shared the candy, and it tasted like heaven. Carly felt like a star because she had run so fast to get the candy.

Answer Each Question.

1 - What did Carly see at the park?

_____

2 - Why did Carly's mom say it was too far away?

_____

3 - Did Carly want to get in the car to go to the jar?

_____

ar

COLOR ME

Read and color the Letter

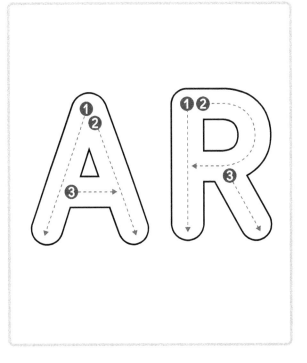

I CAN READ

Read the story, and identify and underline all the - al- words.

Cal Fixes Window

Cal was a small boy who loved animals. He wanted to visit the zoo to see his favorite animal, the bald eagle. His mom said they couldn't go because they needed to fix the broken window. Cal was sad, but then he had an idea. He could fix the window himself! He grabbed his tools and went to work. It took him a while, but he fixed the window. His mom was proud, and they went to the zoo. When they arrived, they saw the bald eagle perched on a branch, looking majestic. It was a beautiful sight, and Cal felt happy he had fixed the window and could see his favorite animal.

Answer Each Question.

Write all the "al" words you can see in the story			

I CAN READ

Read the sentences and answers the questions: Put a check mark

The fox is a speedy animal

The leaves fall gently

Liam went for a long walk

Questions

What animal is known for its speed?   cat ☐   fox ☐

Where Liam went?   long walk ☐   garden ☐

Write the correct word beside each scrambled word.

takl _____	badl _____	paml _____
qualiyt _____	Waltre _____	hatl _____
caml _____	satl _____	alwasy _____

Make sentences

Quality
_____
_____

Talk
_____
_____

Rules
TRACE AND COLOR

Trace it:

AL AL AL AL AL

al al al al

balk balk balk

Colour it:

al

I CAN WRITE

Color Me!

calm

Circle the – al – words

ail	say	also
bald	nail	halt
joan	bald	pay

Trace the words

Fill in the missing letters

tal ____   cal ____

bal ____   alway ____

al ____   almos ____

Read and Trace the sentence.

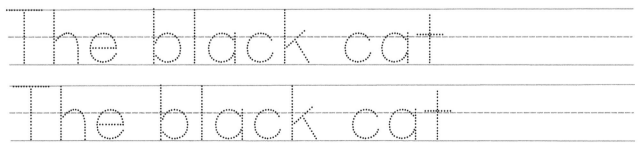

22

al

READ AGAIN

Read the story, and answer each question. highlight the answers in the story.

Cal Fixes Window

Cal was a small boy who loved animals. He wanted to visit the zoo to see his favorite animal, the bald eagle. His mom said they couldn't go because they needed to fix the broken window. Cal was sad, but then he had an idea. He could fix the window himself! He grabbed his tools and went to work. It took him a while, but he fixed the window. His mom was proud, and they went to the zoo. When they arrived, they saw the bald eagle perched on a branch, looking majestic. It was a beautiful sight, and Cal felt happy he had fixed the window and could see his favorite animal.

Answer Each Question.

1 - Why did Cal's mother say they couldn't go to the zoo?

_____

2 - What tools did Cal use to fix the window?

_____

3 - How did Cal feel when he saw the bald eagle at the zoo?

_____

al

COLOR ME

Read and color the Letter

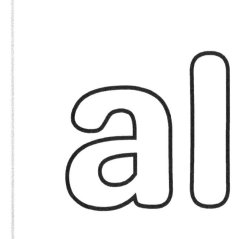

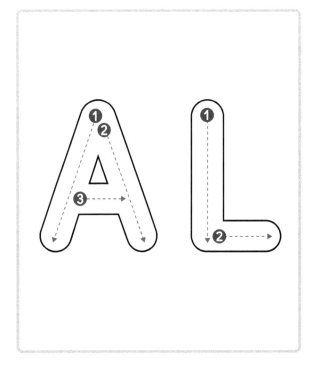

au

I CAN READ

Rescued by Augustus

Once upon a time, there was a naughty little mouse named Paul who lived in a house. One day, he snuck into the kitchen to eat some cheese. But he didn't see that the cheese was in a trap. Suddenly, SNAP! The trap closed on his tail, and Paul cried out in pain. Just then, a kind and wise old mouse named Augustus appeared. Augustus had been caught in traps before and knew just what to do. He helped Paul escape from the trap and showed him how to avoid them in the future. Paul was grateful and promised to never be naughty again.

Answer Each Question.

Write all the "au" words you can see in the story			

au

I CAN READ

Read the sentences and answers the questions: Put a check mark

Lucas flaunts his car

James taunt our team

They will launch rocket to space

Questions

What did Lucas feel?   flaunts his car ☐   worry ☐

What did James do?   run ☐   he taunt our team ☐

Write the correct word beside each scrambled word.

vautl _____	jautn _____	hautn _____
tatu _____	launhc _____	halu _____
Palu _____	vautl _____	dautn _____

Make sentences

Daunt _____

_____

Launch _____

_____

Rules
TRACE AND COLOR

Trace it:

AU AU AU AU

au   au   au   au

laud laud laud

Colour it:

au

I CAN WRITE

Color Me!

taut

Circle the - au - words

ail	laud	also
bald	nail	maul
jaunt	bald	launch

Trace the words

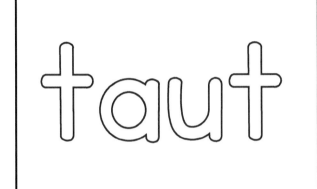

gaunt gaunt
paul   paul
maul   maul

Fill in the missing letters

vautl ____   launhc ____

halu ____   malu ____

jautn ____   ladu ____

Read and Trace the sentence.

We will go to jaunt
We will go to jaunt

READ AGAIN

Read the story, and answer each question. highlight the answers in the story.

Rescued by Augustus

Once upon a time, there was a naughty little mouse named Paul who lived in a house. One day, he snuck into the kitchen to eat some cheese. But he didn't see that the cheese was in a trap. Suddenly, SNAP! The trap closed on his tail, and Paul cried out in pain. Just then, a kind and wise old mouse named Augustus appeared. Augustus had been caught in traps before and knew just what to do. He helped Paul escape from the trap and showed him how to avoid them in the future. Paul was grateful and promised to never be naughty again.

Answer Each Question.

1 - What did Paul want to do when he snuck into the kitchen?

_____

2 - What happened to Paul when he tried to eat the cheese?

_____

3 - Who helped Paul escape from the trap and what did he teach him?

_____

au I CAN WRITE

Color Me!

taut

Circle the - au - words

ail	laud	also
bald	nail	maul
jaunt	bald	launch

Trace the words

gaunt gaunt
paul paul
maul maul

Fill in the missing letters

vautl _____	launhc _____
halu _____	malu _____
jautn _____	ladu _____

Read and Trace the sentence.

We will go to jaunt

We will go to jaunt

28

au

READ AGAIN

Read the story, and answer each question. highlight the answers in the story.

Rescued by Augustus

Once upon a time, there was a naughty little mouse named Paul who lived in a house. One day, he snuck into the kitchen to eat some cheese. But he didn't see that the cheese was in a trap. Suddenly, SNAP! The trap closed on his tail, and Paul cried out in pain. Just then, a kind and wise old mouse named Augustus appeared. Augustus had been caught in traps before and knew just what to do. He helped Paul escape from the trap and showed him how to avoid them in the future. Paul was grateful and promised to never be naughty again.

Answer Each Question.

1 - What did Paul want to do when he snuck into the kitchen?

_____

2 - What happened to Paul when he tried to eat the cheese?

_____

3 - Who helped Paul escape from the trap and what did he teach him?

_____

au

COLOR ME

Read and color the Letter

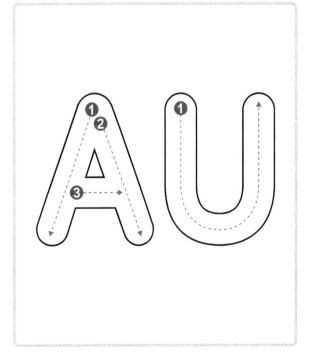

Read the story, and identify and underline all the - oi - words.

Jack's Soil Solution

jack was a farmer who had to toil in his fields all day. He noticed his crops were not growing well due to poor soil. So he boiled water and poured it over the fields to make it healthier. His hard work paid off, and his crops grew stronger. jack invited his friends to join him in celebrating his successful crop. They all sat together, enjoying the delicious food made from jack's harvest. jack was proud to share his hard work and his success with his friends. He knew as well that hard work could lead to great success.

Answer Each Question.

Write all the "oi" words you can see in the story			

I CAN READ

Read the sentences and answers the questions: Put a check mark

I plant a seed in the soil

Lucas dropped a coin

Jack will point out the street on the map

Questions

What Lucas dropped on?   coin ☐   table ☐

What Jack will point out?   map ☐   bird ☐

Write the correct word beside each scrambled word.

soli _____   joni _____   spoli _____

poitn _____   vodi _____   oli _____

coni _____   moits _____   foli _____

Make sentences

Point _____

_____

_____

Join _____

_____

_____

Rules
TRACE AND COLOR

Trace it:

OI   OI   OI   OI   OI   OI

oi   oi   oi   oi

oil   oil   oil   oil

Colour it:

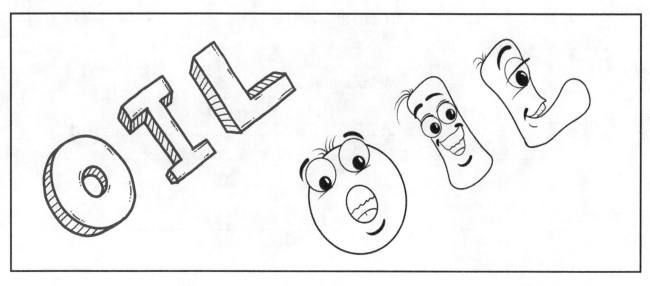

I CAN WRITE

Color Me!

Circle the - oi - words

oil	laud	void
join	nail	coin
loin	bald	point

Trace the words

hoist   hoist
void   void
point   point

Fill in the missing letters

boi _____   voi _____

coi _____   soi _____

loi _____   coi _____

Read and Trace the sentence.

I can bend the joint

I can bend the joint

34

READ AGAIN

Jack's Soil Solution

jack was a farmer who had to toil in his fields all day. He noticed his crops were not growing well due to poor soil. So he boiled water and poured it over the fields to make it healthier. His hard work paid off, and his crops grew stronger. jack invited his friends to join him in celebrating his successful crop. They all sat together, enjoying the delicious food made from jack's harvest. jack was proud to share his hard work and his success with his friends. He knew as well that hard work could lead to great success.

Answer Each Question.

1 - Who is the main character of the story?

_____

2 - How did Jack make the soil healthier?

_____

3 - Did Jack's hard work pay off?

_____

COLOR ME

Read and color the Letter

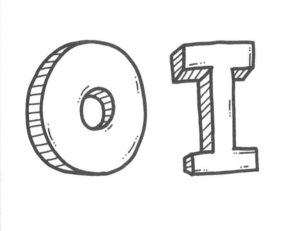

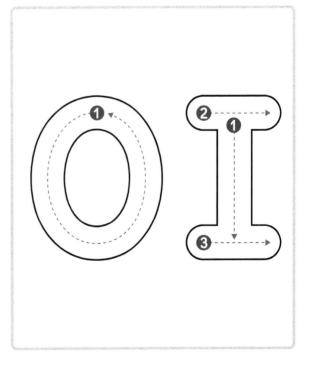

oe
I CAN READ

Bo Trouble Triumph

Bo was on his way to the store when he stubbed his toe on a stone. "Woe is me," he thought. But he didn't let it slow him down. Bo hopped on one foot to the store, where he saw his friend, Doe. Doe was busy using a hoe to weed her garden. "Oh I can help you," said Bo. They worked together, pulling out the weeds one by one. Suddenly, they heard a loud noise. It was a foe, a mischievous fox, trying to steal their vegetables. But Bo and Doe chased him away, laughing and feeling victorious.

Answer Each Question.

Write all the "oe" words you can see in the story			

COLOR ME

Read and color the Letter

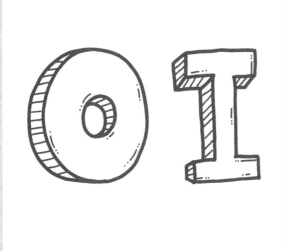

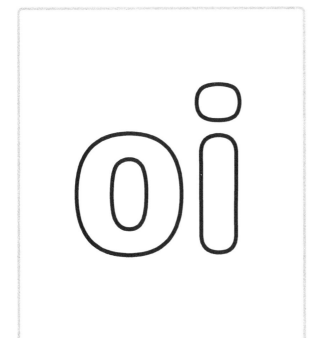

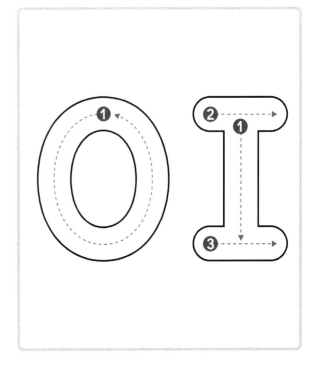

oe

I CAN READ

Bo Trouble Triumph

Bo was on his way to the store when he stubbed his toe on a stone. "Woe is me," he thought. But he didn't let it slow him down. Bo hopped on one foot to the store, where he saw his friend, Doe. Doe was busy using a hoe to weed her garden. "Oh I can help you," said Bo. They worked together, pulling out the weeds one by one. Suddenly, they heard a loud noise. It was a foe, a mischievous fox, trying to steal their vegetables. But Bo and Doe chased him away, laughing and feeling victorious.

Answer Each Question.

Write all the "oe" words you can see in the story			

I CAN READ

Read the sentences and answers the questions: Put a check mark

Human has a ten toes

Lucas goes out to the garden

Ava goes out to the school

Questions

What does a human have?   toes [ ]   map [ ]

Where ava goes out?   restaurant [ ]   school [ ]

Write the correct word beside each scrambled word.

deo _____   heo _____   feo _____

Jeo _____   tipteo _____   tose _____

weo _____   gose _____   weo _____

Make sentences

goes _____

_____

tiptoe _____

_____

Rules
TRACE AND COLOR

Trace it:

OE OE OE OE OE

oe oe oe oe

doe doe doe

Colour it:

I CAN WRITE

Color Me!

Circle the – oe – words

oil	laud	doe
join	toes	coin
goes	woe	point

Trace the words

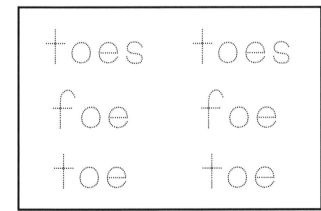

Fill in the missing letters

fo _____   goe _____

wo _____   wo _____

to _____   to _____

Read and Trace the sentence.

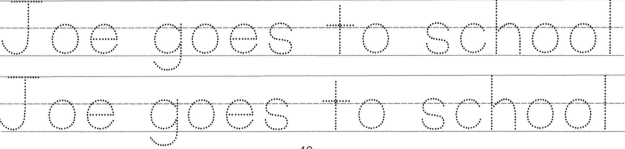

READ AGAIN

Read the story, and answer each question. highlight the answers in the story.

Bo Trouble Triumph

Bo was on his way to the store when he stubbed his toe on a stone. "Woe is me," he thought. But he didn't let it slow him down. Bo hopped on one foot to the store, where he saw his friend, Doe. Doe was busy using a hoe to weed her garden. "Oh I can help you," said Bo. They worked together, pulling out the weeds one by one. Suddenly, they heard a loud noise. It was a foe, a mischievous fox, trying to steal their vegetables. But Bo and Doe chased him away, laughing and feeling victorious.

Answer Each Question.

1 - Who did Bo see at the store?

_____

2 - What did Bo use to hop to the store?

_____

3 - What did Bo and Doe do when they saw the fox?

_____

COLOR ME

Read and color the Letter

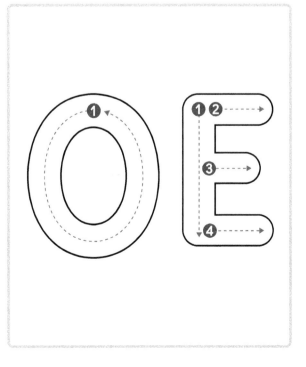

I CAN READ

ow

Read the story, and identify and underline all the - ow - words.

Bity's Bow Knots

There was a cow named Bity who lived on a farm with her owner, a boy named Timmy. Bity loved to roam the fields and munch on the tall grass. But one day, she stumbled upon a bow lying in the grass. She tried to put it on her head, but it kept slipping off. Frustrated, Bity asked Timmy for help. He showed her how to tie the bow properly. Impressed by Timmy's skill, Bity wanted to learn how to tie knots too. Timmy gave her a piece of rope and showed her how to make a knot. From that day on, Bity would often be seen practicing her knots while wearing the bow on her head. Timmy was proud of his clever cow.

Answer Each Question.

Write all the "ow" words you can see in the story			

I CAN READ

Read the sentences and answers the questions: Put a check mark

The clown at the town

My dog had brown hair

I can plow the land

Questions

Where is the clown?	town ☐		school ☐	
What color of dog hair?	brown ☐		blue ☐	

Write the correct word beside each scrambled word.

cwo _____	nwo _____	jolw _____
hwo _____	plwo _____	folw _____
bwo _____	donw _____	wwo _____

Make sentences

cow _____

_____

how _____

_____

Rules
TRACE AND COLOR

Trace it:

OW   OW   OW

ow   ow   ow   ow

bow   bow   bow

Colour it:

45

I CAN READ

Read the sentences and answers the questions: Put a check mark

The clown at the town

My dog had brown hair

I can plow the land

Questions

Where is the clown?	town ☐	school ☐
What color of dog hair?	brown ☐	blue ☐

Write the correct word beside each scrambled word.

cwo _____	nwo _____	jolw _____
hwo _____	plwo _____	folw _____
bwo _____	donw _____	wwo _____

Make sentences

cow _____

_____

how _____

_____

TRACE AND COLOR

Trace it:

OW   OW   OW

ow   ow   ow   ow

bow   bow   bow

Colour it:

I CAN WRITE

Color Me!

Circle the - ow - words

fowl	laud	doe
join	jowl	pow
howl	woe	jowl

Trace the words

plow   plow
gown   gown
howl   howl

Fill in the missing letters

yolw _____   nwo _____

brwo _____   bronw _____

vwo _____   cronw _____

Read and Trace the sentence.

Down the street

Down the street

READ AGAIN

Read the story, and answer each question. highlight the answers in the story.

Bity's Bow Knots

There was a cow named Bity who lived on a farm with her owner, a boy named Timmy. Bity loved to roam the fields and munch on the tall grass. But one day, she stumbled upon a bow lying in the grass. She tried to put it on her head, but it kept slipping off. Frustrated, Bity asked Timmy for help. He showed her how to tie the bow properly. Impressed by Timmy's skill, Bity wanted to learn how to tie knots too. Timmy gave her a piece of rope and showed her how to make a knot. From that day on, Bity would often be seen practicing her knots while wearing the bow on her head. Timmy was proud of his clever cow.

Answer Each Question.

1 - What did Bity stumble upon in the grass?

_____

2 - What did Timmy show Bity how to do?

_____

3 - What did Timmy give to Bity?

_____

COLOR ME

Read and color the Letter

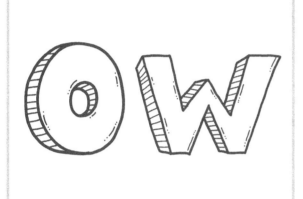

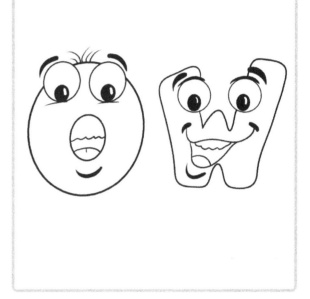

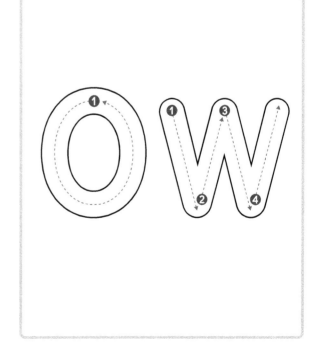

I CAN READ

Read the story, and identify and underline all the - ea - words.

Tea Party Friends

With her plush animals, Luna adored hosting tea parties. For each of her visitors, she would set up a little table and serve tea. She made the decision to include her friend Max one day. Max was eager to attend his first tea party because he had never done it before. Max accepted Luna's offer of tea and cake. This is the nicest cake I've ever tasted, Max remarked after taking a slice. Luna responded with a smile "My mom and I were her helpers. The greatest baker in town is her." They made the decision to start a baking team when Max asked Luna if she could teach him how to bake. They produced delectable desserts like strawberry shortcake and chocolate cream pies.

Answer Each Question.

Write all the "ea" words you can see in the story			

I CAN READ

Read the sentences and answers the questions: Put a check mark

I had a bad dream

Jack has a beard

Ava bought a cheap dress

Questions

What does jack have?   beard ☐   car ☐

What ava bought?   flowers ☐   dress ☐

Write the correct word beside each scrambled word.

clena _____   drema _____   speka _____

dela _____   eta _____   Jena _____

dera _____   sae _____   lefa _____

Make sentences

near _____
_____
_____

meal _____
_____
_____

Rules
TRACE AND COLOR

Trace it:

EA EA EA EA EA

ea ea ea ea

eat eat eat

Colour it:

I CAN WRITE

Color Me!

Circle the - ea - words

beat	laud	dear
join	jean	pow
neat	leaf	jowl

Trace the words

east   east
sear   sear
each   each

Fill in the missing letters

sera _____   fera _____

beda _____   hera _____

clena _____   lefa _____

Read and Trace the sentence.

Great team

Great team

READ AGAIN

Tea Party Friends

With her plush animals, Luna adored hosting tea parties. For each of her visitors, she would set up a little table and serve tea. She made the decision to include her friend Max one day. Max was eager to attend his first tea party because he had never done it before. Max accepted Luna's offer of tea and cake. This is the nicest cake I've ever tasted, Max remarked after taking a slice. Luna responded with a smile "My mom and I were her helpers. The greatest baker in town is her." They made the decision to start a baking team when Max asked Luna if she could teach him how to bake. They produced delectable desserts like strawberry shortcake and chocolate cream pies.

Answer Each Question.

1 - What does Luna enjoy doing with her plush animals?

_____

2 - Who did Luna invite to her tea party for the first time?

_____

3 - What did Max say about the cake Luna served him?

_____

COLOR ME

Read and color the Letter

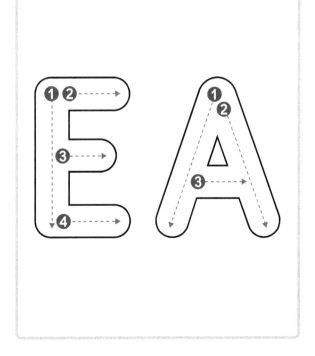

Read the story, and identify and underline all the - ed - words.

Fun at Playground

With her buddies, Molly ran around the playground. They danced outside while clapping their hands. They were startled to see a dog that had scaled the fence. The puppy approached them while waving its tail. With a grin on her face, Molly stroked the dog. The puppy was entertained until it was time to return home. Molly turned back and waved to the dog as they made their way back to their classroom. She grinned once again, appreciative of the enjoyable day she had with her friends and the adorable puppy they had met.

Answer Each Question.

Write all the "ed" words you can see in the story			

I CAN READ

Read the sentences and answers the questions: Put a check mark

I have a bed

Lisa filled her glass with water

Jack saw a lion at the zoo

Questions

| What Lisa she did? | filled her glass ☐ | Bought a car ☐ |
| What did Jack see at the zoo? | dog ☐ | lion ☐ |

Write the correct word beside each scrambled word.

askde _____   aimde _____   stayde _____

fixde _____   yellde _____   cleande _____

helpde _____   playde _____   stayde _____

Make sentences

stayed _____

_____

played _____

_____

Trace it:

ED   ED   ED

ed   ed   ed   ed

acted   acted

Colour it:

I CAN WRITE

Color Me!

Circle the – ed – words

ended	laud	dear
join	planted	pow
missed	leaf	asked

Trace the words

helped helped
passed passed
fixed fixed

Fill in the missing letters

jumpe ____   picke ____

sniffe ____   locke ____

dresse ____   playe ____

Read and Trace the sentence.

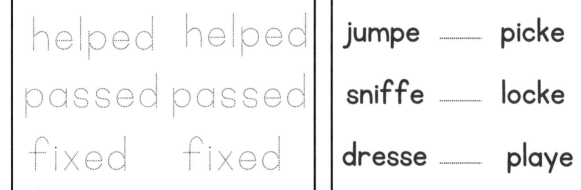

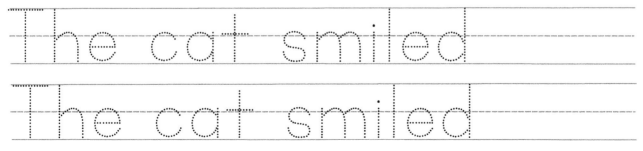

The cat smiled
The cat smiled

READ AGAIN

Fun at Playground

With her buddies, Molly ran around the playground. They danced outside while clapping their hands. They were startled to see a dog that had scaled the fence. The puppy approached them while waving its tail. With a grin on her face, Molly stroked the dog. The puppy was entertained until it was time to return home. Molly turned back and waved to the dog as they made their way back to their classroom. She grinned once again, appreciative of the enjoyable day she had with her friends and the adorable puppy they had met.

Answer Each Question.

1 - What were Molly and her friends doing on the playground?

_____

2 - How did Molly react when she saw the dog?

_____

3 - What did Molly do when it was time to return home?

_____

COLOR ME

Read and color the Letter

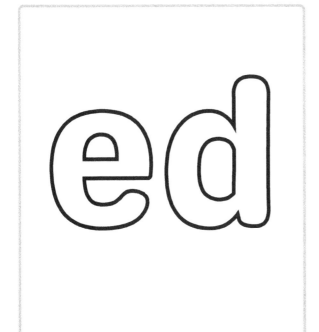

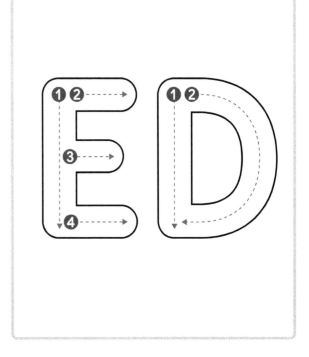

I CAN READ

Read the story, and identify and underline all the - ei- words.

Kate's Reindeer Discovery

Kate was a talented student who enjoyed reading. She once discovered a book with a picture of a sleigh on her shelves. She opened the book and began reading about the Christmas Eve antics of the eight little reindeer who were pulling Santa's sleigh. They were distributing gifts to kids all throughout the world as they soared across the sky, and Kate was mesmerized by their height and speed. She was so absorbed in the narrative that she was completely unaware that her mother had called to ask her to supper.

Answer Each Question.

Write all the "ei" words you can see in the story			

I CAN READ

Read the sentences and answers the questions: Put a check mark

I will receive a box by mail

The cat's vein bulged

She couldn't conceive why

Questions

What happened to the cat's vein?   calm ☐   bulged ☐

What will receive in mail?   flowers ☐   box ☐

Write the correct word beside each scrambled word.

seiez _____   receiev _____   deceti _____

weidr _____   conceti _____   receiev _____

eithre _____   seiez _____   eithre _____

Make sentences

either

_____

_____

weird

_____

_____

Rules
TRACE AND COLOR

Trace it:

E E E

ei ei ei ei

either either

Colour it:

I CAN WRITE

Color Me!

pier

Circle the – ei – words

pier	laud	dear
join	copied	pow
carries	leaf	jowl

Trace the words

siege   siege
pier   pier
pities pities

Fill in the missing letters

carrie ____   eithe ____

copie ____   weir ____

seiz ____   receiv ____

Read and Trace the sentence.

Deceiving animals

deceiving animals

64

READ AGAIN

Read the story, and answer each question. highlight the answers in the story.

Kate's Reindeer Discovery

Kate was a talented student who enjoyed reading. She once discovered a book with a picture of a sleigh on her shelves. She opened the book and began reading about the Christmas Eve antics of the eight little reindeer who were pulling Santa's sleigh. They were distributing gifts to kids all throughout the world as they soared across the sky, and Kate was mesmerized by their height and speed. She was so absorbed in the narrative that she was completely unaware that her mother had called to ask her to supper.

Answer Each Question.

1 - What did Kate discover?

_____

2 - What was on the shelves?

_____

3 - What were the reindeer doing?

_____

COLOR ME

Read and color the Letter

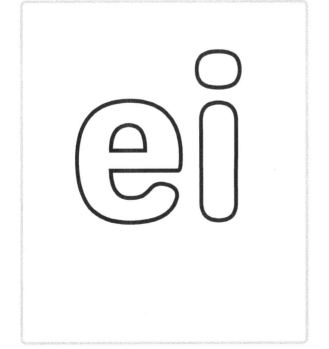

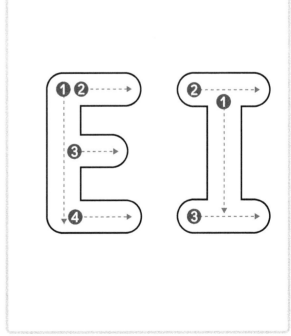

I CAN READ

Read the story, and identify and underline all the - ea- words.

Ernie's Big Race

Eva was a cheerful girl who loved to explore. One day, she stumbled upon a cave while walking in the forest. She was curious and went in to investigate. The cave was eerie, and she could hear strange noises. Suddenly, she saw a glimmer in the darkness. It was a treasure chest! She rushed to open it and found a pearl necklace, a feather, and a leather purse. She felt ecstatic and continued to explore. Soon, she found an eroded rock and etched her name on it. She felt like a true adventurer, and her discoveries made her day unforgettable.

Answer Each Question.

Write all the "er" words you can see in the story			

I CAN READ

Read the sentences and answers the questions: Put a check mark

Luna is a member of a basketball team

Mom read all book chapter

Dad coming to school very faster

Questions

| Does dad come to school | faster ☐ | slow ☐ |
| What mom did? | read ☐ | laugh ☐ |

Write the correct word beside each scrambled word.

towre ———	showre ———	bothre ———
powre ———	lockre ———	rathre ———
angre ———	playre ———	hangre ———

Make sentences

power _____

_____

flower _____

_____

Rules
TRACE AND COLOR

Trace it:

ER   ER   ER

er   er   er   er

tower   tower

Colour it:

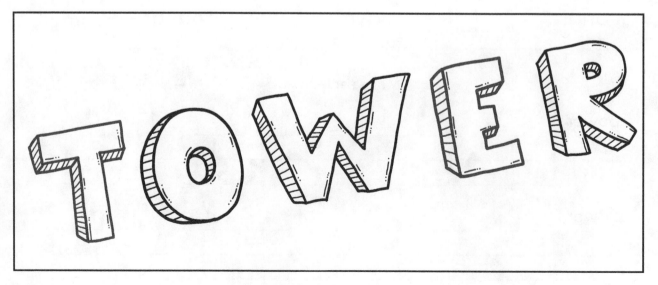

I CAN WRITE

Color Me!

ever

Circle the – er – words

pier	laud	clever
join	ever	pow
river	leaf	sister

Trace the words

tower tower
anger anger
rather rather

Fill in the missing letters

laye _____   eage _____

playe _____   showe _____

seiz _____   longe _____

Read and Trace the sentence.

Mother's dinner

Mother's dinner

70

READ AGAIN

Ernie's Big Race

Eva was a cheerful girl who loved to explore. One day, she stumbled upon a cave while walking in the forest. She was curious and went in to investigate. The cave was eerie, and she could hear strange noises. Suddenly, she saw a glimmer in the darkness. It was a treasure chest! She rushed to open it and found a pearl necklace, a feather, and a leather purse. She felt ecstatic and continued to explore. Soon, she found an eroded rock and etched her name on it. She felt like a true adventurer, and her discoveries made her day unforgettable.

Answer Each Question.

1 - What did Eva discover while walking in the forest?

_____

2 - What did Eva find inside the treasure chest?

_____

3 - How did Eva feel when she found the treasure chest?

_____

COLOR ME

Read and color the Letter

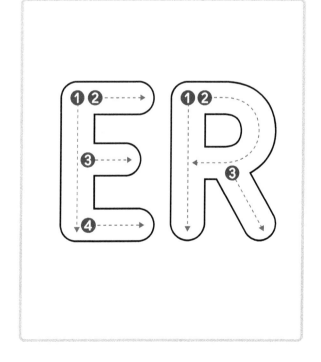

I CAN READ

ee

Read the story, and identify and underline all the - ee- words.

Exploring the Forest

Bee was a cheerful bee who loved to dance. She would sway to the rhythm of the breeze and twirl around flowers. One day, she saw a tree with juicy fruit and decided to get some. As she landed on the branch, she heard a sneeze. It was the tree! "Are you okay?" asked Bee. "I have a cold," replied the tree. Bee knew what to do. She gathered some leaves and made tea. She fed the tree, and it felt better. "Thank you, Bee!" said the tree. "You're welcome, friend!" replied Bee, and they danced together in the breeze.

Answer Each Question.

Write all the "ee" words you can see in the story			

I CAN READ

Read the sentences and answers the questions: Put a check mark

The dessert was sweet

Grandpa has a lot of sheep

Ava listened to the teacher's speech

Questions

How was the dessert?	sweet ☐	spicy ☐
For what ava listened?	speech ☐	laugh ☐

Write the correct word beside each scrambled word.

stele _____   swete _____   beehc _____

stepe _____   befe _____   dere _____

spede _____   bere _____   chepe _____

Make sentences

cheep _____

_____

bee _____

_____

74

Rules
TRACE AND COLOR

Trace it:

E E   E E   E E

e e e e   e e   e e

beef beef beef

Colour it:

I CAN WRITE

Color Me!

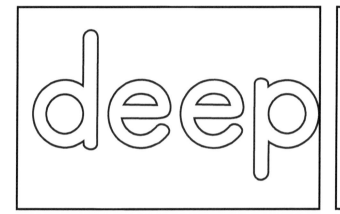

Circle the – ee – words

pier	laud	bleed
steel	deep	pow
deem	leaf	cheer

Trace the words

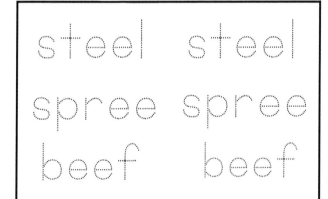

Fill in the missing letters

beec _____   bree _____

breec _____   blee _____

chee _____   flee _____

Read and Trace the sentence.

Nice to meet you

Nice to meet you

READ AGAIN

Read the story, and answer each question. highlight the answers in the story.

Exploring the Forest

Bee was a cheerful bee who loved to dance. She would sway to the rhythm of the breeze and twirl around flowers. One day, she saw a tree with juicy fruit and decided to get some. As she landed on the branch, she heard a sneeze. It was the tree! "Are you okay?" asked Bee. "I have a cold," replied the tree. Bee knew what to do. She gathered some leaves and made tea. She fed the tree, and it felt better. "Thank you, Bee!" said the tree. "You're welcome, friend!" replied Bee, and they danced together in the breeze.

Answer Each Question.

1 - What did Bee see on the tree?

_____

2 - What did Bee do to help the tree?

_____

3 - How did the tree feel after Bee helped it?

_____

COLOR ME

Read and color the Letter

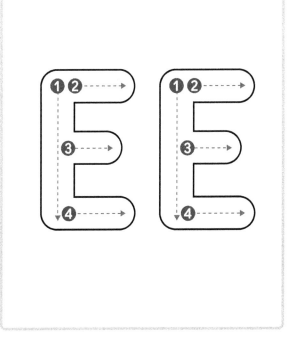

ear

I CAN READ

The Brave Deer

Pearl loved to hear stories from her grandpa. He would tell her tales of faraway lands and magical creatures. One day, as they were walking in the park, they heard a strange noise. It was coming from the bushes. Pearl was scared, but her grandpa reassured her and they went to investigate. As they got closer, they saw a little bear cub stuck in a trap. Pearl's grandpa carefully freed the cub, and they were relieved to see it was unharmed. The cub looked at them with big, grateful eyes and then ran off into the woods. Pearl and her grandpa walked home, happy to have helped a furry friend.

Answer Each Question.

Write all the "ear" words you can see in the story			

I CAN READ

Read the sentences and answers the questions: Put a check mark

Carl works hard to earn more money

I get up early today

Ava would like to learn how to drive a bike

Questions

Why did carl work hard?   earn money ☐   play ☐

What ava would like to do?   learn how to drive ☐   running ☐

Write the correct word beside each scrambled word.

earht _____   yeanr _____   earnets _____

pealr _____   headr _____   searhc _____

leanr _____   earyl _____   ealr _____

Make sentences

search _____

_____

_____

earn _____

_____

_____

Rules
TRACE AND
COLOR

Trace it:

EAR EAR EAR

ear ear ear ear

learn learn learn

Colour it:

I CAN WRITE

Color Me!

earn

Circle the – ear – words

pier	earth	bleed
steel	earn	early
deem	learn	cheer

Trace the words

early   early
heard   heard
learn   learn

Fill in the missing letters

lear	searc ....
eart	earl ....
hear	pear ....

Read and Trace the sentence.

Big ears hear all

Big ears hear all

READ AGAIN

Read the story, and answer each question. highlight the answers in the story.

The Brave Deer

Pearl loved to hear stories from her grandpa. He would tell her tales of faraway lands and magical creatures. One day, as they were walking in the park, they heard a strange noise. It was coming from the bushes. Pearl was scared, but her grandpa reassured her and they went to investigate. As they got closer, they saw a little bear cub stuck in a trap. Pearl's grandpa carefully freed the cub, and they were relieved to see it was unharmed. The cub looked at them with big, grateful eyes and then ran off into the woods. Pearl and her grandpa walked home, happy to have helped a furry friend.

Answer Each Question.

1 - What did Pearl love to do with her grandpa?

_____

2 - What did Pearl and her grandpa hear in the park?

_____

3 - What did Pearl's grandpa do to help the bear cub?

_____

COLOR ME

Read and color the Letter

ie
I CAN READ

Read the story, and identify and underline all the - ie - words.

Helping the Bird

There was a little girl named Badie who loved to lie in the grass and watch the clouds float by. One day, she saw a bird with a broken wing lying on the ground. Badie brought the bird home to her mother. "What happened to this little bird?" asked her mother. "I don't know," replied Badie. "But we have to help it!" Her mother agreed, and they took the bird to the vet. The vet said the bird needed a special diet to help its wing heal. Badie and her mother bought the food. They took care of the bird and eventually, its wing healed. Badie was happy to have helped the bird and it made her feel proud of herself.

Answer Each Question.

Write all the "ie" words you can see in the story			

I CAN READ

Read the sentences and answers the questions: Put a check mark

A helmet can shield you from the accident

Lucas took a piece of pizza

Medicine can relieve the pain

Questions

What did Lucas take?	piece of pizza ☐	bike ☐
What medicine can do?	relieve the pain ☐	cat ☐

Write the correct word beside each scrambled word.

pire _____   belife _____   fiedn _____

pieec _____   relife _____   brife _____

nieec _____   grife _____   nieec _____

Make sentences

friend _____

_____

_____

piece _____

_____

_____

Rules
TRACE AND COLOR

Trace it:

IE   IE   IE

ie   ie   ie   ie

chief chief chief

Colour it:

I CAN WRITE

Color Me!

pier

Circle the – ie – words

pier	earth	piece
steel	belief	early
relief	learn	fiend

Trace the words

chief chief
brief brief
cities cities

Fill in the missing letters

citie ____   copie ____

frien ____   sieg ____

cashie ____   studie ____

Read and Trace the sentence.

I studied hard

I studied hard

READ AGAIN

Read the story, and answer each question. highlight the answers in the story.

Helping the Bird

There was a little girl named Badie who loved to lie in the grass and watch the clouds float by. One day, she saw a bird with a broken wing lying on the ground. Badie brought the bird home to her mother. "What happened to this little bird?" asked her mother. "I don't know," replied Badie. "But we have to help it!" Her mother agreed, and they took the bird to the vet. The vet said the bird needed a special diet to help its wing heal. Badie and her mother bought the food. They took care of the bird and eventually, its wing healed. Badie was happy to have helped the bird and it made her feel proud of herself.

Answer Each Question.

1 - What did Badie see lying on the ground one day?

_____

2 - Who did Badie bring the bird home to?

_____

3 - Who bought the special food for the bird's diet?

_____

COLOR ME

Read and color the Letter

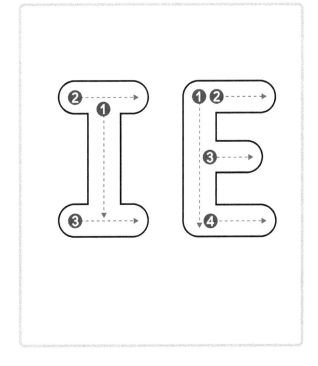

ir

I CAN READ

Read the story, and identify and underline all the - ir - words.

The Quirky Bears

The first bear was thirsty so he went to stir the pot, hoping the porridge would be ready in no time. The second bear was tired so he went to sleep.The third bear was hungry and pleaded with the first bear. "I'm hungry, please cook faster!" The porridge was ready and the two bears enjoyed themselves.When the third bear woke up, he found that the porridge was over and there were dirty bowls on the sink. He was so hungry but since the porridge mix was over, he called a fairy who granted him one wish.

Answer Each Question.

Write all the "ir" words you can see in the story			

91

I CAN READ

Read the sentences and answers the questions: Put a check mark

The dragon's lair was hidden

I will go up the stairs

Luna has a chair in her room

Questions

What luna did have?   chair ☐   car ☐

What was hidden?   dragon's lair ☐   bike ☐

Write the correct word beside each scrambled word.

chari _____   hari _____   stari _____

ari _____   lari _____   blari _____

flari _____   pari _____   fari _____

Make sentences

chair _____
- -
_____

stair _____
- -
_____

Trace it:

IR   IR   IR

ir   ir   ir   ir

hair   hair   hair

Colour it:

I CAN WRITE

Color Me!

Circle the – ir – words

pier	chair	piece
chair	lair	early
pair	learn	air

Trace the words

chair   chair
hair   hair
stair   stair

Fill in the missing letters

stai ___	chai ___
hai ___	lai ___
stai ___	pai ___

Read and Trace the sentence.

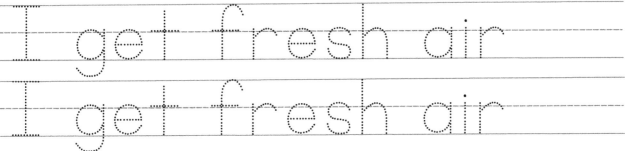

I get fresh air
I get fresh air

94

READ AGAIN

The Quirky Bears

The first bear was thirsty so he went to stir the pot, hoping the porridge would be ready in no time. The second bear was tired so he went to sleep.The third bear was hungry and pleaded with the first bear. "I'm hungry, please cook faster!" The porridge was ready and the two bears enjoyed themselves.When the third bear woke up, he found that the porridge was over and there were dirty bowls on the sink. He was so hungry but since the porridge mix was over, he called a fairy who granted him one wish.

Answer Each Question.

1 - The fairy granted a wish.
Question: Who granted a wish?

_____

2 - The bear stirred porridge.
Question: What did the bear do to the porridge?

_____

3 - The bear found dirt.
Question: What did the bear find?

_____

COLOR ME

Read and color the Letter

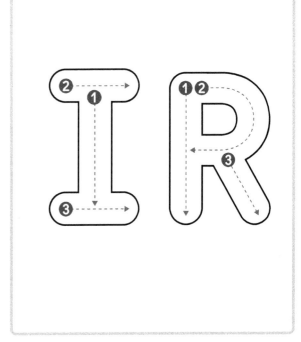

id

I CAN READ

Read the story, and identify and underline all the - id - words.

Learning to Ride

Once upon a time, Ben wanted to learn how to ride a bike. He tried and tried, but he kept falling off. He felt frustrated and wanted to give up. But then his dad came and said, "Don't give up, Ben. I'll help you." His dad held the bike steady as Ben pedaled. It was hard, but Ben didn't give up. After a few tries, he started to balance and ride on his own. Ben was thrilled and felt proud of himself. He learned that sometimes we need help from others, but with persistence and practice, we can accomplish anything we set our minds to.

Answer Each Question.

Write all the "id" words you can see in the story			

I CAN READ

Read the sentences and answers the questions: Put a check mark

Mom let the lid drop on the pan

He did not stop the bus

Lucas slide onto the ice

Questions

What is mom did do?   let the lid drop ☐   running ☐

What happened to Lucas?   slide onto the ice ☐   play ☐

Write the correct word beside each scrambled word.

ddi _____   sdi _____   kdi _____

sldi _____   hdi _____   hdi _____

skdi _____   rdi _____   squdi _____

Make sentences

kid _____

_____

did _____

_____

Rules
TRACE AND COLOR

Trace it:

ID ID ID

id id id id

hid hid hid

Colour it:

id

I CAN WRITE

Color Me!

slid

Circle the – id – words

slid	chair	did
skid	lair	hid
rid	kid	air

Trace the words

kids kids

squid squid

sid sid

Fill in the missing letters

stai ____   chai ____

hai ____   lai ____

stai ____   pai ____

Read and Trace the sentence.

Happy playing kids

Happy playing kids

READ AGAIN

Read the story, and answer each question. highlight the answers in the story.

Learning to Ride

Once upon a time, Ben wanted to learn how to ride a bike. He tried and tried, but he kept falling off. He felt frustrated and wanted to give up. But then his dad came and said, "Don't give up, Ben. I'll help you." His dad held the bike steady as Ben pedaled. It was hard, but Ben didn't give up. After a few tries, he started to balance and ride on his own. Ben was thrilled and felt proud of himself. He learned that sometimes we need help from others, but with persistence and practice, we can accomplish anything we set our minds to.

Answer Each Question.

1 - What did Ben want to learn how to do?

_____

2 - How did Ben feel when he kept falling off the bike?

_____

3 - What did Ben learn from this experience?

_____

COLOR ME

Read and color the Letter

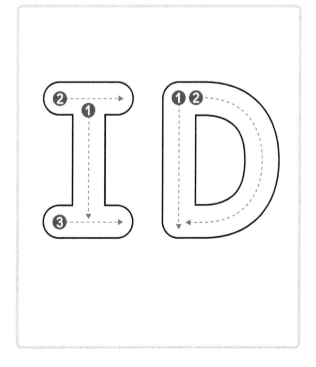

Read the story, and identify and underline all the - sp- words.

Spotty's Shiny Discovery

Spotty the dog loved to dig in the dirt. He dug and dug until he found something shiny. It was a spoon! Spotty picked it up with his mouth and ran to show his owner. She was surprised and happy to see the shiny spoon. She told Spotty that it was special and belonged to her grandmother. Spotty felt proud to have found something so important. His owner thanked him and gave him a big hug. From that day on, Spotty didn't just dig in the dirt, he also looked for special treasures that could bring happiness to his owner.

Answer Each Question.

Write all the "sp" words you can see in the story			

I CAN READ

Read the sentences and answers the questions: Put a check mark

Mom, give me a hot spud

Luna saw a spot on the rug

The house has speed wifi

Questions

What did mom give?　　　hot spud ☐　　　book ☐

What does the house have?　speed wifi ☐　　garden ☐

Write the correct word beside each scrambled word.

spna ———　　　spnu ———　　　spti ———

spde ———　　　spta ———　　　spdu ———

spni ———　　　spot ———　　　spede ———

Make sentences

speed _____

_____

spot _____

_____

Rules
TRACE AND COLOR

Trace it:

SP   SP   SP

sp   sp   sp   sp

spat   spat   spat

Colour it:

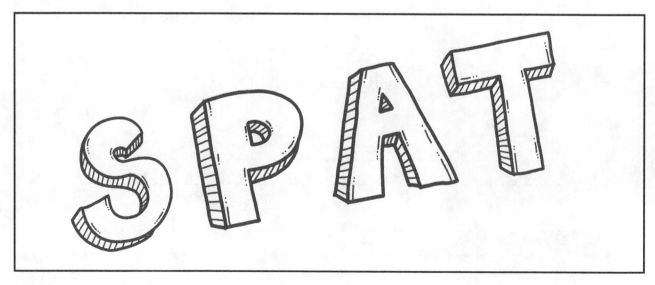

I CAN WRITE

Color Me!

spin

Circle the – sp – words

spot	laud	dear
join	spin	spun
neat	leaf	span

Trace the words

span   span
spot   spot
spud   spud

Fill in the missing letters

sppe _____	spu _____
spo _____	spi _____
spu _____	spa _____

Read and Trace the sentence.

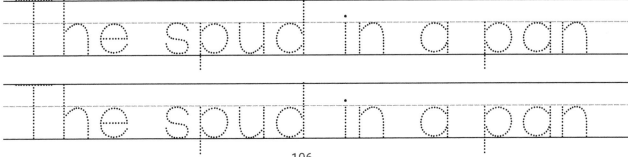

The spud in a pan

The spud in a pan

READ AGAIN

Spotty's Shiny Discovery

Spotty the dog loved to dig in the dirt. He dug and dug until he found something shiny. It was a spoon! Spotty picked it up with his mouth and ran to show his owner. She was surprised and happy to see the shiny spoon. She told Spotty that it was special and belonged to her grandmother. Spotty felt proud to have found something so important. His owner thanked him and gave him a big hug. From that day on, Spotty didn't just dig in the dirt, he also looked for special treasures that could bring happiness to his owner.

Answer Each Question.

1 - What did Spotty find when he was digging in the dirt?

_____

2 - How did Spotty feel after he found the shiny object?

_____

3 - Who did Spotty show the shiny spoon to?

_____

COLOR ME

Read and color the Letter

sh
I CAN READ

Dora the Fish

Dora loved the deep blue waters but nothing made her more happy than watching the ships pass by. The other fishes would warn her about the fishermen who would kidnap fish only to eat them but she didn't care. Her only wish was to see the other side of the world where there was dry land. One day, a fisherman caught her and she was put in an aquarium where people would come to watch her.Days passed and she missed her family. She regretted not listening to them when they warned her.At the Aquarium, she made friends with a young boy who visited her often and promised to help set her free, which he did and she reunited with her family.

Answer Each Question.

Write all the "sh" words you can see in the story			

109

I CAN READ

Read the sentences and answers the questions: Put a check mark

Luna went on a big ship

Dad has a gash on his hand

I must set the lid on the trash

Questions

Luna went on	big ship ☐		bus ☐	
Dad has a	book ☐		gash ☐	

Write the correct word beside each scrambled word.

fihs _____   cahs _____   clahs _____

muhs _____   bahs _____   flahs _____

bruhs _____   rahs _____   trahs _____

Make sentences

cash _____

_____

_____

shop _____

_____

_____

Rules
TRACE AND
COLOR

Trace it:

SH   SH   SH

sh   sh   sh   sh

shop   shop   shop

Colour it:

I CAN WRITE

Color Me!

ship

Circle the – sh – words

spot	ship	dear
shut	spin	shift
cash	leaf	lash

Trace the words

dash   dash
rash   rash
slash   slash

Fill in the missing letters

slas _____   sho _____

las _____   sho _____

das _____   sha _____

Read and Trace the sentence.

I have a cash

I have a cash

READ AGAIN

Dora the Fish

Dora loved the deep blue waters but nothing made her more happy than watching the ships pass by. The other fishes would warn her about the fishermen who would kidnap fish only to eat them but she didn't care. Her only wish was to see the other side of the world where there was dry land. One day, a fisherman caught her and she was put in an aquarium where people would come to watch her. Days passed and she missed her family. She regretted not listening to them when they warned her. At the Aquarium, she made friends with a young boy who visited her often and promised to help set her free, which he did and she reunited with her family.

Answer Each Question.

1 - The fish was saved.
Question: Who was saved?

_____

2 - The ship passed.
Question: What passed by?

_____

3 - The fisherman caught fish.
Question: Who caught fish?

_____

113

COLOR ME

Read and color the Letter

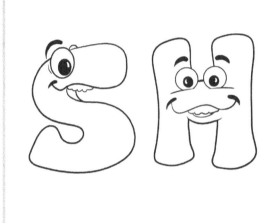

I CAN READ

Read the story, and identify and underline all the - sh- words.

Scary Scavenger Hunt

Sally loved to dance and her favorite music was the Scottish tunes. She would put on her special scarf and skip and hop around her room, pretending to be a Scottish dancer. One day, her school was having a talent show and Sally wanted to perform a Scottish dance. She asked her dad to help her practice and he played the bagpipes for her. Sally worked hard and practiced every day. On the day of the talent show, Sally danced beautifully to the Scottish music. The crowd cheered and clapped for her. Sally felt proud of herself and knew that with practice and dedication, she could achieve anything she set her mind to.

Answer Each Question.

Write all the "sc" words you can see in the story			

I CAN READ

Read the sentences and answers the questions: Put a check mark

The cut got a scab

Dad scan the barcode

The cat scats the dog

0 00035 54562 0

Questions

What dad did do?   play ☐   scan the barcode ☐

The cat   run away ☐   scats the dog ☐

Write the correct word beside each scrambled word.

scba ———   scto ———   scrbu ———

scta ———   scna ———   scrpa ———

scma ———   scrma ———   scba ———

Make sentences

scam _____
_____
_____

scat _____
_____
_____

Rules
TRACE AND COLOR

Trace it:

SC   SC   SC

sc   sc   sc   sc

scot   scot   scot

Colour it:

I CAN WRITE

Color Me!

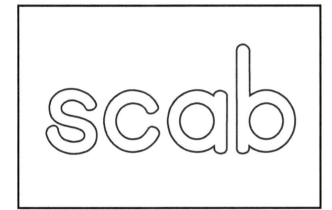

Circle the – sc – words

spot	ship	dear
scat	scab	scot
scrub	leaf	lash

Trace the words

scan   scan

scat   scat

scam   scam

Fill in the missing letters

sca ——————   scru ——————

sco ——————   sca ——————

scra ——————   sco ——————

Read and Trace the sentence.

Scan the code

Scan the code

118

READ AGAIN

Scary Scavenger Hunt

Sally loved to dance and her favorite music was the Scottish tunes. She would put on her special scarf and skip and hop around her room, pretending to be a Scottish dancer. One day, her school was having a talent show and Sally wanted to perform a Scottish dance. She asked her dad to help her practice and he played the bagpipes for her. Sally worked hard and practiced every day. On the day of the talent show, Sally danced beautifully to the Scottish music. The crowd cheered and clapped for her. Sally felt proud of herself and knew that with practice and dedication, she could achieve anything she set her mind to.

Answer Each Question.

1 - What is Sally's favorite type of music?

_____

2 - What does Sally use when she dances in her room?

_____

3 - What does Sally learn about achieving her goals?

_____

COLOR ME

Read and color the Letter

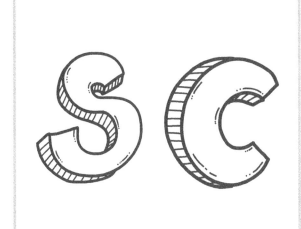

Read the story, and identify and underline all the - br- words.

The Brave Bunny

Freddy was a friendly frog who loved to explore the forest. One day, he hopped over to a beautiful pond where he met Francesca, a fancy frilled lizard. Francesca was feeling sad because she had lost her frill, which she thought was the most beautiful part of her body. Freddy decided to help her find it. They searched high and low until they found it tangled in a bush. Freddy carefully untangled the frill and helped Francesca put it back on. She was thrilled and grateful to Freddy for his help. From that day on, Francesca and Freddy became good friends and went on many more adventures together.

Answer Each Question.

Write all the "br" words you can see in the story			

I CAN READ

Read the sentences and answers the questions: Put a check mark

James brags his car

The blue hat has a big brim

A brat hit ava

Questions

What did James do?	play ☐	brags his car ☐
The blue hat has	big brim ☐	scats the dog ☐

Write the correct word beside each scrambled word.

brga _____	brna _____	brta _____
brta _____	brda _____	brmi _____
brmi _____	brde _____	brda _____

Make sentences

brag _____

_____

bran _____

_____

Rules
TRACE AND COLOR

Trace it:

BR   BR   BR

br   br   br   br

brim   brim   brim

Colour it:

I CAN WRITE

Color Me!

brim

Circle the - br - words

spot	brag	dear
brim	scab	scot
bred	leaf	brad

Trace the words

brag	brag
brim	brim
bran	bran

Fill in the missing letters

bra ____	bre ____
bri ____	bra ____
bra ____	bre ____

Read and Trace the sentence.

Bran bun

bran bun

READ AGAIN

The Brave Bunny

Freddy was a friendly frog who loved to explore the forest. One day, he hopped over to a beautiful pond where he met Francesca, a fancy frilled lizard. Francesca was feeling sad because she had lost her frill, which she thought was the most beautiful part of her body. Freddy decided to help her find it. They searched high and low until they found it tangled in a bush. Freddy carefully untangled the frill and helped Francesca put it back on. She was thrilled and grateful to Freddy for his help. From that day on, Francesca and Freddy became good friends and went on many more adventures together.

Answer Each Question.

1 - Where did Freddy meet Francesca?

_____

2 - Where did they find Francesca's frill?

_____

3 - What happened after they found the frill?

_____

COLOR ME

Read and color the Letter

Read the story, and identify and underline all the - pl- words.

Happy Hoppy Friends

Polly had a plan to plant a pretty plant in her backyard. She grabbed a shovel and dug a deep hole. Then she plucked a small plant from a pot and placed it in the hole. She patted the soil and said, "Please grow, plant!" But the plant did not grow. Polly was sad, but then she remembered something her mom told her. "Plants need light to grow!" So Polly picked up the plant and placed it in a sunny spot. The plant began to grow tall and beautiful. Polly was thrilled, her plan worked!

Answer Each Question.

Write all the "pl" words you can see in the story			

I CAN READ

Read the sentences and answers the questions: Put a check mark

Mom had a plum

Grandpa had a crop on a plot

The crab can plod

Questions

Mom had	plum	☐	car	☐
The crab can	plod	☐	run	☐

Write the correct word beside each scrambled word.

plna _____   plde _____   plto _____

pldo _____   plpo _____   plsu _____

plmu _____   plgu _____   plna _____

Make sentences

plan

_____

_____

plod

_____

_____

Trace it:

Pl   Pl   Pl   Pl   Pl   Pl

pl   pl   pl   pl

plan   plan   plan

Colour it:

I CAN WRITE

Color Me!

plod

Circle the - pl - words

plod	brag	pled
brim	plod	scot
plop	leaf	plus

Trace the words

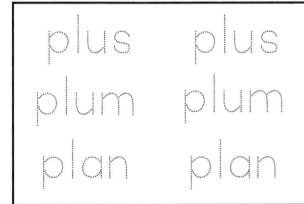

plus   plus

plum   plum

plan   plan

Fill in the missing letters

pla ____	ple ____
plo ____	plo ____
plu ____	plu ____

Read and Trace the sentence.

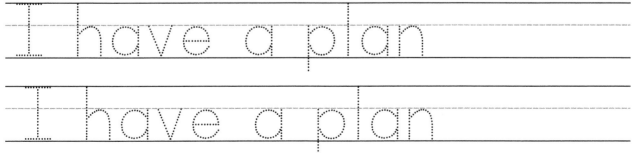

I have a plan

I have a plan

READ AGAIN

Read the story, and answer each question. highlight the answers in the story.

Happy Hoppy Friends

Polly had a plan to plant a pretty plant in her backyard. She grabbed a shovel and dug a deep hole. Then she plucked a small plant from a pot and placed it in the hole. She patted the soil and said, "Please grow, plant!" But the plant did not grow. Polly was sad, but then she remembered something her mom told her. "Plants need light to grow!" So Polly picked up the plant and placed it in a sunny spot. The plant began to grow tall and beautiful. Polly was thrilled, her plan worked!

Answer Each Question.

1 - What was Polly's plan?

_____

2 - Why was Polly sad when the plant did not grow?

_____

3 - What did Polly remember that her mom had told her?

_____

COLOR ME

Read and color the Letter

I CAN READ

Read the story, and identify and underline all the - bl - words.

Blue Balloon Adventure

Billy had a blue balloon. He blew and blew until it was big. But then, he accidentally let it go. The balloon flew away into the blue sky. Billy was sad, so he went to his friend Blake's house. "I lost my balloon," said Billy with a frown. "I have an idea," said Blake with a grin. They went outside and saw a big blue blanket. They both held the blanket and blew air into it. Soon, the blanket filled with air and lifted them both up, higher and higher into the sky. They giggled and floated, just like Billy's lost blue balloon.

Answer Each Question.

Write all the "bl" words you can see in the story			

I CAN READ

Read the sentences and answers the questions: Put a check mark

Ava doesn't blab at anyone

The cut bled a lot

He doesn't blame me

Questions

Ava Doesn't	blab	☐	kidding	☐
He doesn't	plod	☐	blame	☐

Write the correct word beside each scrambled word.

blma _____	blpi _____	blde _____
blba _____	blbo _____	blba _____
blde _____	blto _____	blma _____

Make sentences

blam _____
_____
_____

blob _____
_____
_____

Rules
TRACE AND COLOR

Trace it:

B B B B B B B B

b b b b

blot blot blot

Colour it:

I CAN WRITE

Color Me!

blab

Circle the - bl - words

blab	blam	pled
blip	plod	blot
plop	leaf	plus

Trace the words

blam	blam
bled	bled
blot	blot

Fill in the missing letters

blo ___	bli ___
bla ___	blo ___
ble ___	bli ___

Read and Trace the sentence.

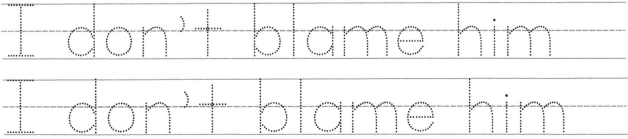

I don't blame him
I don't blame him

READ AGAIN

Blue Balloon Adventure

Billy had a blue balloon. He blew and blew until it was big. But then, he accidentally let it go. The balloon flew away into the blue sky. Billy was sad, so he went to his friend Blake's house. "I lost my balloon," said Billy with a frown. "I have an idea," said Blake with a grin. They went outside and saw a big blue blanket. They both held the blanket and blew air into it. Soon, the blanket filled with air and lifted them both up, higher and higher into the sky. They giggled and floated, just like Billy's lost blue balloon.

Answer Each Question.

1 - What happened to Billy's blue balloon?

_____

2 - Who did Billy go to for help after losing his balloon?

_____

3 - What did Billy and Blake do with the blue blanket?

_____

COLOR ME

Read and color the Letter

gl

I CAN READ

Gloria the glamorous Piggy

Gloria the glamorous piggy wore her glittery tiara and pink gloves. She loved looking pretty and found new ways to improve her looks. "Gloria! You look amazing!" Other piggies would compliment her and she glowed every time she was appreciated.Her biggest dream was to join a beauty pageant and so, she signed up.She was glad that they accepted her as one of the contestants and celebrated by drinking a glass of milk before bed.

Answer Each Question.

Write all the "gl" words you can see in the story			

I CAN READ

Read the sentences and answers the questions: Put a check mark

There is a big glen in the village

I am glad to see my friends

I am not glum

Questions

There is a big	glen ☐	mountune ☐
I am not	glum ☐	blame ☐

Write the correct word beside each scrambled word.

glda _____	glne _____	glbi _____
glbi _____	glbo _____	glda _____
glmu _____	gltu _____	glmu _____

Make sentences

glad _____

_____

_____

glum _____

_____

_____

Rules

TRACE AND COLOR

Trace it:

GL   GL   GL   GL   GL

gl   gl   gl   gl

glad   glad   glad

Colour it:

I CAN WRITE

Color Me!

glob

Circle the – gl – words

blab	glum	pled
glob	plod	glut
plop	glib	plus

Trace the words

glib   glib
glad   glad
glut   glut

Fill in the missing letters

glu _____   gle _____

gla _____   glo _____

glu _____   gla _____

Read and Trace the sentence.

Glen in the fog

glen in the fog

READ AGAIN

Gloria the glamorous Piggy

Gloria the glamorous piggy wore her glittery tiara and pink gloves. She loved looking pretty and found new ways to improve her looks. "Gloria! You look amazing!" Other piggies would compliment her and she glowed every time she was appreciated.Her biggest dream was to join a beauty pageant and so, she signed up.She was glad that they accepted her as one of the contestants and celebrated by drinking a glass of milk before bed.

Answer Each Question.

1 - Gloria was glamorous.
Question: How was gloria?

_____

2 - Gloria enjoyed the glory.
Question: What did Gloria enjoy?

_____

3 - Gloria liked glitters.
Question: What did Gloria like?

_____

143

COLOR ME

Read and color the Letter

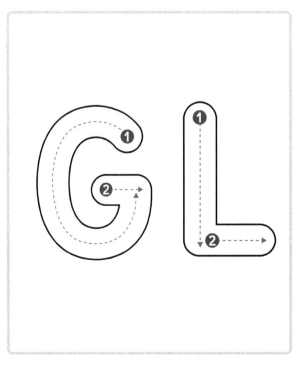

dr
I CAN READ

Read the story, and identify and underline all the - dr - words.

Dragon's Dream Drive

Dragon had a dream to drive a race car. He worked hard and saved up to buy one. He put on his driving gloves and revved up the engine. Dragon drove fast and turned left and right. But then, the car stopped. Dragon looked down and saw a flat tire. He was sad, but then he remembered that he had a spare tire in the trunk. He changed the tire and kept driving. Dragon won the race and was thrilled. He drove back to his cave, feeling proud and happy that he didn't let a flat tire stop him from reaching his dream.

Answer Each Question.

Write all the "dr" words you can see in the story			

I CAN READ

Read the sentences and answers the questions: Put a check mark

I have a drum

She let the lid drop

Ava can drag spot the pup

Questions

I have a   drum ☐   car ☐

She let the lid   drop ☐   drip ☐

Write the correct word beside each scrambled word.

drpi _____   drpo _____   drpi _____

drba _____   drga _____   drgu _____

drgu _____   drmu _____   drba _____

Make sentences

drip _____

_____

drop _____

_____

Rules
TRACE AND COLOR

Trace it:

D R   D R   D R   D R

dr   dr   dr   dr

drum drum drum

Colour it:

I CAN WRITE

Color Me!

drip

Circle the – dr – words

drip	glum	drop
drug	plod	drab
drag	glib	drum

Trace the words

drum   drum
drip   drip
drug   drug

Fill in the missing letters

dru _____   dro _____

dri _____   dru _____

dra _____   dri _____

Read and Trace the sentence.

She played drums

She played drums

READ AGAIN

Read the story, and answer each question. highlight the answers in the story.

Dragon's Dream Drive

Dragon had a dream to drive a race car. He worked hard and saved up to buy one. He put on his driving gloves and revved up the engine. Dragon drove fast and turned left and right. But then, the car stopped. Dragon looked down and saw a flat tire. He was sad, but then he remembered that he had a spare tire in the trunk. He changed the tire and kept driving. Dragon won the race and was thrilled. He drove back to his cave, feeling proud and happy that he didn't let a flat tire stop him from reaching his dream.

Answer Each Question.

1 - What was Dragon's dream?

_____

2 - How did Dragon save up for his race car?

_____

3 - How did Dragon feel after he won the race?

_____

COLOR ME

Read and color the Letter

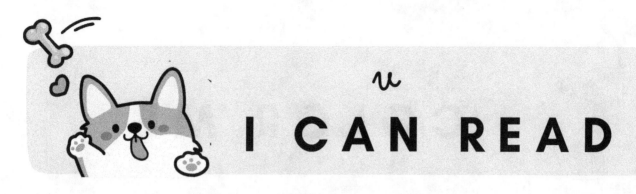
Read the story, and identify and underline all the - v - words.

Vory the Vulture

Vory the vulture loved having a clean house. He would vacuum his house until it was spotless, add flowers in his vases to make his home smell nice and play violin to relax. During the weekend, he would wear his green vest, take his vehicle and go to the mountains to have an adventure. One day, he even saw the volcano erupt which was beautiful and scary at the same time. Generally, Vory lived a happy and simple life filled with small pleasures.

Answer Each Question.

Write all the "v" words you can see in the story			

I CAN READ

Read the sentences and answers the questions: Put a check mark

My dad is a bus driver

Mom bought a vase

He gives me five books

Questions

My dad is a bus   driver ☐   drop ☐

Mom bought a   vase ☐   drip ☐

Write the correct word beside each scrambled word.

fiev _____   evre _____   visibel _____

rivre _____   covre _____   valeu   _____

levle _____   visti _____   voet   _____

Make sentences

visit

_____

- -

_____

villa

_____

- -

_____

TRACE AND COLOR

Trace it:

V   V   V   V

v   v   v   v

vent   vent   vent

Colour it:

I CAN WRITE

Color Me!

move

Circle the – v – words

move	glum	vent
save	drive	drab
civil	glib	value

Trace the words

save   save
voice   voice
river   river

Fill in the missing letters

rive ____   leve ____

ven ____   bevle ____

seve ____   vaes ____

Read and Trace the sentence.

Brave lion

brave lion

154

READ AGAIN

Vory the Vulture

Vory the vulture loved having a clean house. He would vacuum his house until it was spotless, add flowers in his vases to make his home smell nice and play violin to relax. During the weekend, he would wear his green vest, take his vehicle and go to the mountains to have an adventure. One day, he even saw the volcano erupt which was beautiful and scary at the same time. Generally, Vory lived a happy and simple life filled with small pleasures.

Answer Each Question.

1 - Vory wore his vest.
Question: What did Vory wear?

_____

2 - Vory saw a volcano.
Question: What did Vory see?

_____

3 - Vory drove his vehicle?
Question: What did Vory drive?

_____

COLOR ME

Read and color the Letter

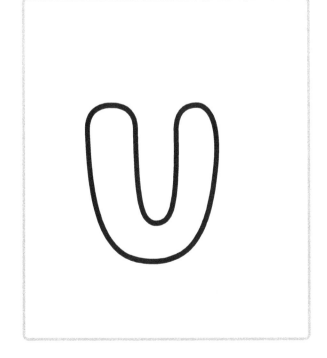

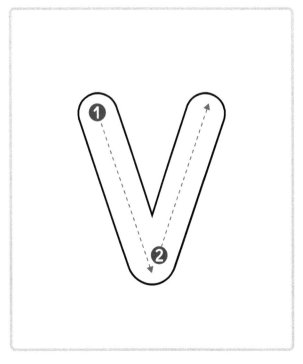

I CAN READ

Walter the Walrus

Walter the walrus loved drinking water or any fruits that had a lot of water. He would eat watermelons and oranges too!As he walked, he would wiggle his body, making his friend Melanie the whale wallow while laughing cheerfully. "Walter! That's incredible!" She would exclaim."Thank you, my friend!" Walter would reply. Walter had a white sweater that he wore during winter. Whenever he played in the snow, other walruses would play with him. This made him very happy.

Answer Each Question.

Write all the "w" words you can see in the story			

I CAN READ

Read the sentences and answers the questions: Put a check mark

An eagle can swoop down

I draw a sketch of my dog

She saw flaws in the seam of the dress

Questions

An eagle can swoop	down	☐	drop	☐
She saw	flaws	☐	cat	☐

Write the correct word beside each scrambled word.

flwa _____	flwa _____	cwa _____
pwa _____	danw _____	balw _____
drwa _____	rwa _____	bralw _____

Make sentences

paw _____

_____

_____

flaw _____

_____

_____

Rules
TRACE AND COLOR

Trace it:

W   W   W   W

w   w   w   w

owl   owl   owl

Colour it:

I CAN WRITE

Color Me!

jaw

Circle the – w – words

jaw	glum	bow
save	plow	drab
chow	brown	value

Trace the words

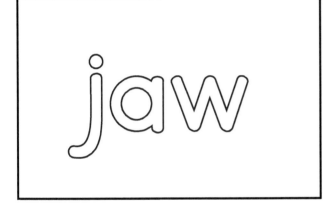

chow   chow
how   how
town   town

Fill in the missing letters

tow ____   no ____

plo ____   wo ____

tow ____   jow ____

Read and Trace the sentence.

Town had parks

Town had parks

160

READ AGAIN

Walter the Walrus

Walter the walrus loved drinking water or any fruits that had a lot of water. He would eat watermelons and oranges too!As he walked, he would wiggle his body, making his friend Melanie the whale wallow while laughing cheerfully. "Walter! That's incredible!" She would exclaim."Thank you, my friend!" Walter would reply. Walter had a white sweater that he wore during winter. Whenever he played in the snow, other walruses would play with him. This made him very happy.

Answer Each Question.

1 - Walter's favorite color was white.
Question: What was Walter's favorite color?

_____

2 - Walter wore sweaters during winter.
Question: When did Walter wear sweaters.

_____

3 - Walter wiggled his body.
Question: What did he do with his body?

_____

COLOR ME

Read and color the Letter

Read the story, and identify and underline all the - x - words.

The Foxes of Max

Max and his dog, Ox, went for a walk in the park. Max saw a box and decided to take a peek. Inside, he found six red foxes! Ox barked at the foxes, but they didn't seem to mind. Max decided to take them home. At home, Max put the foxes in a pen. They started to play with each other. Max sat and watched them for a while. The foxes were so cute! Max decided to keep them and named them Red, Xander, Dixie, Coy, and Zax. Max and Ox loved their new furry friends.

Answer Each Question.

Write all the "x" words you can see in the story			

I CAN READ

Read the sentences and answers the questions: Put a check mark

I received a box

They go to the apex

She saw flaws in the seam of the dress

Questions

I received	a bike ☐	a box ☐
They go to	apex ☐	space ☐

Write the correct word beside each scrambled word.

axu ————	axle ————	affxi ————
bxo ————	axli ————	dxo ————
apxe ————	alexni ————	cxo ————

Make sentences

box
_____
- - - - - - - - - - - - - - - - - - -
_____

dox
_____
- - - - - - - - - - - - - - - - - - -
_____

Rules
TRACE AND COLOR

Trace it:

X   X   X   X

x   x   x   x

box   box   box

Colour it:

I CAN WRITE

Color Me!

aux

Circle the - x - words

box	glum	bow
save	cox	ex
dux	aux	value

Trace the words

ox   ox
dox   dox
axe   axe

Fill in the missing letters

o ____   bo ____

do ____   wo ____

ax ____   jo ____

Read and Trace the sentence.

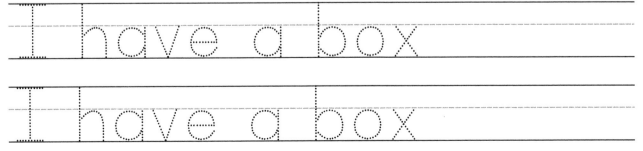

I have a box

I have a box

READ AGAIN

The Foxes of Max

Max and his dog, Ox, went for a walk in the park. Max saw a box and decided to take a peek. Inside, he found six red foxes! Ox barked at the foxes, but they didn't seem to mind. Max decided to take them home. At home, Max put the foxes in a pen. They started to play with each other. Max sat and watched them for a while. The foxes were so cute! Max decided to keep them and named them Red, Xander, Dixie, Coy, and Zax. Max and Ox loved their new furry friends.

Answer Each Question.

1 - What was Ox's reaction when he saw the foxes inside the box?

_____

2 - What did Max do with the foxes when he took them home?

_____

3 - How did the foxes react when they were put in a pen?

_____

COLOR ME

Read and color the Letter

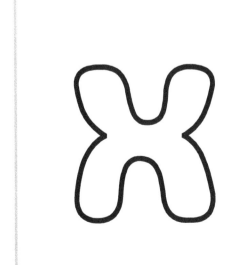

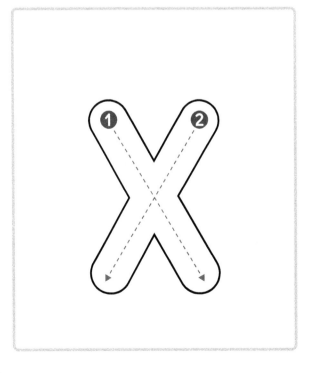

I CAN READ

Read the story, and identify and underline all the - y - words.

Yellow Bird Adventure

Once upon a time, there was a friendly yellow bird named Yoyo. Yoyo loved to fly and explore new places. One day, Yoyo flew to a nearby yard and saw a yummy yellow yam. Yoyo decided to take a bite, but then realized it belonged to someone else. Feeling guilty, Yoyo flew away. As Yoyo continued to fly, a young boy named Yanni saw her and was amazed by her beautiful yellow feathers. Yoyo chirped happily and flew around Yanni, showing off her feathers. Yanni smiled and waved at Yoyo. From that day on, Yoyo and Yanni became great friends and would play together in the yard every day.

Answer Each Question.

Write all the "y" words you can see in the story			

I CAN READ

Read the sentences and answers the questions: Put a check mark

She has a gray hair

We are a brave boys

They pay a tax

Questions

She has a   gray hair ☐   a book ☐

They pay   money ☐   a tax ☐

Write the correct word beside each scrambled word.

plya _____   gya _____   hya _____

pya _____   dya _____   clya _____

bya _____   sya _____   swya _____

Make sentences

bay _____

_____

play _____

_____

Trace it:

Y   Y   Y   Y

y   y   y   y

bay   bay   bay

Colour it:

I CAN WRITE

Color Me!

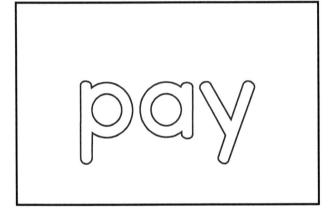

Circle the – y – words

box	pay	bow
play	gay	say
slay	aux	hay

Trace the words

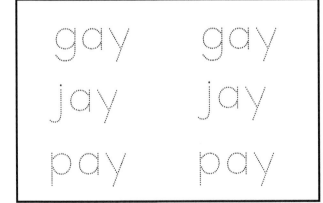

gay   gay

jay   jay

pay   pay

Fill in the missing letters

swa ____	da ____
sla ____	wa ____
ja ____	na ____

Read and Trace the sentence.

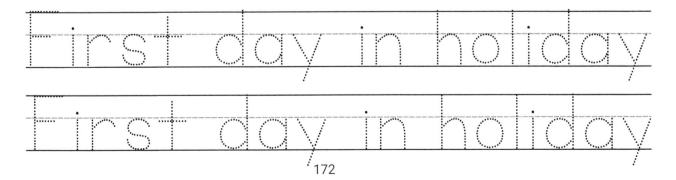

First day in holiday

First day in holiday

172

READ AGAIN

Yellow Bird Adventure

Once upon a time, there was a friendly yellow bird named Yoyo. Yoyo loved to fly and explore new places. One day, Yoyo flew to a nearby yard and saw a yummy yellow yam. Yoyo decided to take a bite, but then realized it belonged to someone else. Feeling guilty, Yoyo flew away. As Yoyo continued to fly, a young boy named Yanni saw her and was amazed by her beautiful yellow feathers. Yoyo chirped happily and flew around Yanni, showing off her feathers. Yanni smiled and waved at Yoyo. From that day on, Yoyo and Yanni became great friends and would play together in the yard every day.

Answer Each Question.

1 - What was the name of the friendly yellow bird in the story?

_____

2 - What did Yoyo see in the nearby yard?

_____

3 - Why did Yoyo feel guilty after taking a bite of the yellow yam?

_____

COLOR ME

Read and color the Letter

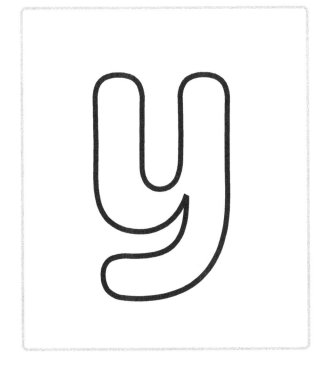

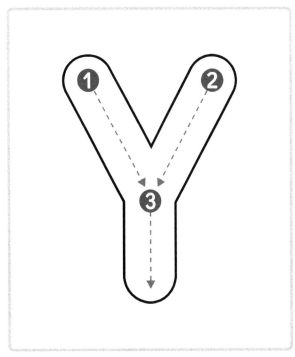

I CAN READ

Zara the Zebra

Zara the Zebra went to the Zoo. She came from Africa and had to travel a long way to get there. She felt a little dizzy because the truck moved up and down, like a zigzag. The Zookeeper was kind and gave her food to eat, but Zara missed her home. At first, she didn't have any friends, but then she made new ones and started having fun at the Zoo. She was happy to learn that the Zebra-crossing was named after Zebras like her.

Answer Each Question.

Write all the "z" words you can see in the story			

175

I CAN READ

Read the sentences and answers the questions: Put a check mark

There was a jazz band in the restaurant

Fizzy juice tastes good

Zooming train goes by

Questions

There was a	jazz band	☐	a book	☐
What tastes good and is fizzy?	juice	☐	pizza	☐

Write the correct word beside each scrambled word.

bzuz	_____	fziz	_____	jzaz
fzuz	_____	az	_____	oz
jzaz	_____	si	_____	uz

Make sentences

buzz
_____
_____

jazz
_____
_____

Trace it:

z z z z

z z z z

jazz   jazz   jazz

Colour it:

I CAN WRITE

Color Me!

Circle the - z - words

box	fizz	bow
buzz	gay	fizz
jazz	aux	hay

Trace the words

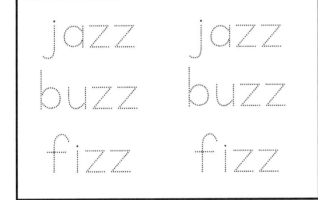

jazz   jazz
buzz   buzz
fizz   fizz

Fill in the missing letters

fiz _____   jaz _____

buz _____   na _____

fiz _____   o _____

Read and Trace the sentence.

Jazz band

jazz band

READ AGAIN

Zara the Zebra

Zara the Zebra went to the Zoo. She came from Africa and had to travel a long way to get there. She felt a little dizzy because the truck moved up and down, like a zigzag. The Zookeeper was kind and gave her food to eat, but Zara missed her home. At first, she didn't have any friends, but then she made new ones and started having fun at the Zoo. She was happy to learn that the Zebra-crossing was named after Zebras like her.

Answer Each Question.

1 - How did Zara feel during the truck ride to the Zoo?

_____

2 - Was the Zookeeper kind to Zara?

_____

3 - Did Zara make any friends at the Zoo?

_____

COLOR ME

Read and color the Letter

THANK YOU

Thank you for choosing this decodable book for your child in first grade. I appreciate your trust in my work and I hope this book will prove to be a valuable tool in your child's reading journey.

As a writer, my goal has always been to create resources that promote reading and make it an enjoyable experience for young readers. This book is designed to help struggling readers improve their decoding skills and gain confidence in their reading abilities.

I have taken a structured approach in this book, teaching children the sounds that letters make in a specific order. I have also included activities in each passage that are designed to reinforce phonemic awareness and promote skill development. My hope is that with the help of this book, your child will build a solid foundation in reading and become a confident and proficient reader in no time.

Once again, thank you for choosing this book. I would love to hear your feedback on this book and how it has helped your child. Your opinion matters to me and it will assist me in creating more valuable resources for young readers in the future.

Thank you for your support and happy reading!

Best regards,

[Jed Dolton]

Printed in the USA
CPSIA information can be obtained
at www.ICGtesting.com
LVHW081313201023
761672LV00018B/1478